WARRIORS
RAVENPAW'S PATH

Created by
ERIN HUNTER

Written by
DAN JOLLEY

Art by
JAMES L. BARRY

SCHOLASTIC INC.

Warriors: Ravenpaw's Path
Created by Erin Hunter
Written by Dan Jolley
Art and Colorization by James L. Barry

Digital Tones - Lincy Chan
Lettering - Lucas Rivera (vol. 1)
- John Hurt (vol. 2 and 3)
Cover Design - Louis Csontos

Editor - Jenna Winterberg (vol. 1)
- Lillian Diaz-Przybyl (vol. 2 and 3)
Managing Editor - Vy Nguyen
Art Director - Al-Insan Lashley

ISBN 978-1-338-55135-8

12 11 10 9 8 7 6 5 4 3 2 1   19 20 21 22 23 24

Printed in the U.S.A.   40

First Scholastic printing, January 2019

CONTENTS

WARRIORS

RAVENPAW'S PATH

1: SHATTERED PEACE

I'VE NEVER KNOWN ANY OTHER NAME FOR THIS PLACE.

I ALWAYS THOUGHT THE FARM NEVER CHANGED.

IT'S JUST...THE FARM.

THAT IT WOULD ALWAYS BE EASY, AND SAFE, AND PERFECT.

SOON ENOUGH, I'D FIND OUT THAT I COULDN'T HAVE BEEN MORE WRONG.

THINGS ARE VERY SIMPLE HERE.

SLEEP, HUNT, EAT...

NOT THAT I REALLY HAVE TO HUNT, NOT WITH ALL THE MICE IN THE BARN.

THE TWOLEGS THAT LIVE HERE AREN'T TOO BAD. THEY LEAVE US ALONE; WE LEAVE THEM ALONE.

EVEN THE DOGS ARE ALL RIGHT. THEY'RE JUST NOISY MORE THAN ANYTHING ELSE.

EVERYTHING HAPPENS THE SAME HERE, EVERY DAY. RIGHT NOW, I KNOW THE TWOLEG IS ABOUT TO COME OUT ON HIS BIG MONSTER.

AND THERE HE GOES.

THE FEMALE TWOLEG IS A LITTLE FRIENDLIER THAN THE MALE.

SHE KNOWS WE LIVE HERE, AND EVERY ONCE IN A WHILE SHE THROWS OUT SOME TWOLEG FOOD FOR US.

I LIKE MICE BETTER.

MY NAME'S RAVENPAW.

I LIVE HERE WITH MY BEST FRIEND, BARLEY.

BLINK BLINK

I GUESS I COULD HAVE TRIED TO GO BACK TO THUNDERCLAN AFTER WHAT HAPPENED WITH BLOODCLAN.

A BUNCH OF VICIOUS CATS FROM TWOLEGPLACE...THEY TRIED TO TAKE OVER THE FOREST LAST GREENLEAF, BUT THEY FAILED.

TIGERCLAW--NOW CALLED TIGERSTAR--HAD BEEN KILLED BY THEIR LEADER.

BARLEY AND I FOUGHT WITH THE CLANS THEN.

BARLEY EVEN KNEW SOME OF THE BLOODCLAN CATS. THEY'D TERRORIZED HIM BEFORE.

IT'S A MIRACLE WE LIVED THROUGH IT. A LOT OF CATS DIDN'T.

TURNED OUT THAT THE FARM WAS THE PLACE FOR ME, THOUGH. IT'S SO MUCH EASIER HERE.

NO TRAINING, NO BORDER PATROLS...NO GOING HUNGRY. IT MIGHT NOT BE HOME, EXACTLY...

...BUT I CAN WAKE UP WHEN I WANT, NOBODY TELLS ME WHAT TO DO...AND BARLEY'S HERE. WE OWE EACH OTHER OUR LIVES.

I FIGURE I'LL STAY.

CONGRATS ON THE MOUSE, THERE, BARLEY.

I CAN ALWAYS COUNT ON YOU AND YOUR FRIEND TO KEEP THE RODENTS IN CHECK.

WE HAVE NO IDEA WHAT THOSE NOISES MEAN.

TWOLEGS ARE STRANGE. BUT LIKE I SAID, THEY DON'T BOTHER US, WE DON'T BOTHER THEM—AND WE STAY CLEAR OF THEIR NEST.

PART OF THE REASON I LIKE IT HERE SO MUCH IS THAT BARLEY AND I CAN GO OUT FOR WALKS.

NOT HUNTING, NOT LOOKING FOR RIVAL CATS...JUST WALKS.

IT'S NICE.

BARLEY IS NICE ENOUGH TO DROP THE SUBJECT.

WE SPEND THE DAY CLEANING UP A LITTLE.

Y'KNOW, IF I WERE STILL A CLAN WARRIOR, I'D HAVE AN APPRENTICE TO DO STUFF LIKE THIS FOR ME.

OH YEAH?

IS THERE ANYTHING ELSE YOU MISS? ABOUT THE CLAN?

NOPE.

THIS PLACE SUITS ME MUCH BETTER THAN THE FOREST.

PLUS, YOU KNOW, **YOU** ARE MY BEST FRIEND.

ALL RIGHT.

RELAX, BARLEY. I'M NOT GOING ANYWHERE.

ME? HEY, I'M TOTALLY RELAXED. YOU'RE THE ONE GETTING ALL SENTIMENTAL. MAYBE **YOU** SHOULD RELAX.

THEN...THAT NIGHT...
SOMETHING BESIDES
THE SNOW ARRIVES
AT THE FARM.

SKRITCH

DID YOU
HEAR
THAT?

YEAH.

DO YOU
KNOW WHAT
IT WAS?

NO. LET'S
GO CHECK
IT OUT.

IT'S REALLY LUCKY WILLIE AND HIS FRIENDS FIND US WHEN THEY DO.

THEY'VE BARELY EVEN FINISHED THEIR FRESH-KILL...

...WHEN MINTY GIVES BIRTH.

EVERYONE...

...THIS IS SNOWFLAKE, AND ICICLE, AND CLOUDY, AND SNIFF.

I CAN'T TAKE MY EYES OFF THEM. I'VE...I'VE JUST FORGOTTEN.

FORGOTTEN HOW BEAUTIFUL KITS CAN BE— LIKE THE KITS BACK IN THUNDERCLAN.

OUR VISITORS SETTLE IN FOR A FEW DAYS, SPENDING ALL THEIR TIME TAKING CARE OF THE KITS.

BARLEY AND I ARE MORE THAN HAPPY TO DO THEIR HUNTING FOR THEM.

RAVENPAW, YOU'RE BACK!

LOOK, KITTENS! RAVENPAW'S BRINGING FOOD FOR US!

HE'S LETTING ME MAKE PLENTY OF MILK FOR YOU!

MEEP!

THE VISITORS ALWAYS HIDE FROM THE TWOLEGS. I TRY TO TELL THEM IT'S OKAY, BUT THEY'RE FIRM ABOUT IT.

IT REALLY IS ALL RIGHT. THEY WON'T BOTHER US.

I'M SORRY, RAVENPAW, IT'S JUST...WE'VE HAD SOME BAD EXPERIENCES WITH TWOLEGS.

OLD HABITS DIE HARD, YOU KNOW.

THE WEATHER GETS BETTER PRETTY FAST.

...BUT MORE IMPORTANT, THE KITS ARE GETTING STRONGER, AND I DON'T WANT TO CHANCE THEM GETTING SICK.

I DON'T MIND THE EXTRA HUNTING SO MUCH. THERE ARE PLENTY OF MICE IN THE BARN...

THE CLAN KITS USED TO LOVE FEATHERS AND SCRAPS OF MOSS, SO I TRY TO FIND NEW ONES FOR THESE KITS TO PLAY WITH.

THEY LOVE ME! I CAN TELL.

IT JUST SEEMS NATURAL TO KEEP DOING THE HUNTING FOR THEM, TOO.

HEY, RAVENPAW, YOU GOT THAT FRESH-KILL FOR US YET?

ON MY WAY, SNAPPER!

WELL, IF YOU COULD HURRY UP WITH IT, THAT'D BE GREAT. WE'RE GETTING HUNGRY.

DON'T YOU WORRY. I'LL HAVE A MOUSE FOR YOU IN NO TIME FLAT!

I DON'T KNOW WHAT'S BOTHERING BARLEY ABOUT WILLIE AND THE OTHER VISITORS.

I THINK THEY'RE GREAT. WILLIE ESPECIALLY--HE'S ALWAYS SO INTERESTED IN HOW THE FARM WORKS...

...EVEN IF HE DOESN'T UNDERSTAND EVERYTHING TO BEGIN WITH.

WILLIE! HEY, WILLIE!

YES, RAVENPAW?

YOU CAN'T ACTUALLY GET OUT OF THE BARN THAT WAY.

UP HERE, THIS JUST CONNECTS TO THE PLACE WHERE THE CHICKENS LIVE.

ALL RIGHT. SO...?

WELL, WE DON'T HUNT THE CHICKENS. IT ISN'T LIKE OUT IN THE WILD.

HERE, THEY BELONG TO THE TWOLEGS, SO WE LEAVE THEM ALONE.

OH...SO YOU DON'T HUNT THEM AT ALL? EVER?

NOPE, NOT EVER. WE DON'T EVEN THINK OF THEM AS PREY.

THAT'S SIMPLY THE WAY IT IS.

ALL RIGHT, THEN. IF YOU DON'T HUNT THEM, NEITHER WILL WE.

I'M REALLY GLAD YOU'RE HERE TO EXPLAIN THINGS LIKE THIS TO US.

SEEMS LIKE THE FARM IS A VERY UNDERSTANDING, VERY--WELL, A VERY LOGICAL PLACE TO LIVE.

YEAH, I GUESS SO.

BARLEY AND I LIKE IT, ANYWAY.

I START NOTICING THAT I'M SEEING BARLEY LESS AND LESS. DON'T KNOW WHAT HE'S OFF DOING...

BUT I HARDLY HAVE TIME TO WORRY ABOUT IT. TOO MUCH FRESH-KILL TO CATCH FOR OUR VISITORS!

HERE, LIKE THIS. MAKE SURE YOUR CLAWS ARE ALL THE WAY OUT...

...AND AIM FOR THE THROAT. THAT'LL PUT THE OTHER CAT DOWN FOR GOOD.

HERE, PRACTICE ON THESE DEAD MICE.

I'LL TELL YOU IF YOU'RE DOING IT RIGHT.

YES, SNAPPER!

THE NEXT TIME I GET A CHANCE TO CHAT WITH MY BEST FRIEND, HE'S STILL ON THE SAME RIDICULOUS SUBJECT.

I'M TELLING YOU, HE WAS TEACHING THEM *DEATH BLOWS!* WHO TEACHES DEATH BLOWS TO KITS?

PLUS, HE TOLD THEM TO PLAY WITH THEIR FOOD! THAT'S FORBIDDEN BY THE WARRIOR CODE, ISN'T IT?

THIS IS NONSENSE, BARLEY. YOU MUST HAVE SEEN ONE THING AND THOUGHT YOU SAW ANOTHER.

SNAPPER WAS PROBABLY JUST TRYING TO TIRE THEM OUT, SO THEY'D SLEEP BETTER.

BUT...BUT...

THOSE KITS ARE PRECIOUS, BARLEY. WE HAVE TO PROTECT THEM AND HELP THE OTHER CATS AS BEST WE CAN.

IF YOU'RE NOT WILLING TO DO THAT, FINE. BUT I'M GOING TO.

THEN, A QUARTER MOON AFTER THEY ARRIVED, WILLIE SPRINGS A SURPRISE OF HIS OWN ON ME.

RAVENPAW, LISTEN, YOU'VE BEEN SO GOOD TO US...

...BUT WE THINK IT'S TIME WE MOVED ON.

M-MOVED ON? YOU MEAN, YOU'RE LEAVING?

BUT...BUT THE KITS...

THAT'S THE THING. THE KITS ARE STRONG ENOUGH TO WALK NOW.

31

AND WE CAN'T JUST STAY HERE AND SOAK UP YOUR GENEROSITY FOREVER.

WE HAVE TO MAKE OUR OWN WAY IN THE WORLD.

I...I GUESS I UNDERSTAND THAT.

BUT YOU COULD STAY HERE, YOU KNOW.

SERIOUSLY. AS LONG AS YOU WANTED TO.

RAVENPAW!

OH, LITTLE ONES! I'LL MISS YOU.

RAVENPAW! RAVENPAW!

IT'S BEEN AN HONOR, WATCHING SUCH FINE KITS GROW.

GOOD LUCK, WILLIE. YOU AND YOUR FRIENDS ALWAYS WILL BE WELCOME HERE.

YES, GOOD LUCK.

I HOPE YOU FIND A PLACE TO CALL YOUR OWN SOON.

I APPRECIATE THAT, BARLEY. AND SOMETHING TELLS ME WE WILL.

DO WE HAVE TO GO? CAN'T WE STAY?

PLEASE? PLEASE, PLEASE, PLEASE?

KITS! YOUR FATHER SAID TO COME ON!

YES, SNAPPER.

WHAT IF BARLEY IS RIGHT? WHAT IF I AM A CLAN CAT, DEEP DOWN?

I DON'T KNOW. THE ONLY THING I DO KNOW...

...IS THAT I MISS THOSE KITS SO MUCH THAT IT'S KILLING ME.

sniff sniff

SPARK

HMM. FUNNY SCENT.

SPARK

SPARK

szizzle

PIECE OF HAY MUST'VE GOTTEN STUCK ON THAT TWOLEG LIGHT OUTSIDE.

THE AIR IS HORRIBLE AS WE DIG, FILLED WITH THE STENCH OF DOGS AND BURNING WOOD...

ROARING FLAMES...

HEAT...

THE METAL IS SO HOT THAT IT STARTS TO BURN MY PAWS, BUT WE DON'T GIVE UP. AND FINALLY...

...IT STARTS TO COME LOOSE.

BARLEY AND I HEAR SOMETHING HOWLING, SOMETHING REALLY BIG, AND IT'S GETTING CLOSER!

BUT ALL WE CAN THINK ABOUT IS GETTING OFF THAT ROOF. AND THE NEAREST, COOLEST WAY TO DO THAT...

...IS TO ENTER THE TWOLEG NEST.

IT'S LIKE SOME KIND OF NIGHTMARE IN THERE.

I KNOW THE TWOLEGS MUST BE HAPPY LIVING IN A NEST LIKE THIS...

...BUT I DON'T EVER WANT TO COME BACK IN HERE AGAIN!

NOT **EVER.**

WE BETTER GO SEE WHAT'S HAPPENING.

HAH...UH-HAH... UH-HAH...

UGH! EVERYTHING SMELLS LIKE SMOKE.

ARE YOU ALL RIGHT?

WOW! THAT'S MORE TWOLEGS THAN I'VE EVER SEEN IN ONE PLACE BEFORE.

I HOPE THEY'RE NOT HERE TO STAY.

YEAH. I THINK SO.

HEY, LOOK-- THE DOGS ARE SAFE.

AND ARE THEY EVER GOING TO THANK US? NO.

THEY'RE DOGS, RAVENPAW. IT'S NOT AS IF THEY'RE GOING TO TALK TO US.

YEAH, YEAH, I KNOW. UNGRATEFUL MUTTS...

SCRATCH
SCRATCH

THE NEXT FEW DAYS ARE TOUGH.

THE BARN IS STILL STANDING, YES--

FLAP FLAP FLAPETTA

--BUT IT IS TOO WRECKED TO USE AS A PROPER HOME.

NOT TO MENTION, THE THING THE TWOLEGS PUT ACROSS THE TOP MAKES SO MUCH NOISE--

--IT'S SCARED ALMOST ALL THE MICE AWAY.

FOR THE FIRST TIME SINCE I GOT HERE...

...FOOD IS SCARCE.

BAHR-AHR-AHR-AHR-AHR!

YOU WERE RIGHT.

THEY **ARE** UNGRATEFUL MUTTS.

NO MORE LEISURELY WALKS FOR US. NOW WE HAVE TO WORK HARD TO FIND ENOUGH FOOD.

AND A FEW DAYS AFTER THE FIRE, WE FIND SOMETHING ELSE, TOO.

RAVENPAW?

YEAH?

COME TAKE A LOOK AT THIS, WOULD YOU?

I'M ASSUMING YOU DIDN'T KILL THAT RABBIT?

WASN'T ME.

COULD IT HAVE BEEN A FOX?

MAYBE, BUT THERE'S NO SCENT OF ONE.

'COURSE, IT'S BEEN RAINING SO MUCH, IT'S HARD TO TELL.

WE DON'T THINK TOO MUCH ABOUT THE DEAD RABBIT TO BEGIN WITH. BUT THEN...

WHAT IS IT?

A...A SCENT. I THOUGHT I...

NAH. I THOUGHT I RECOGNIZED IT, BUT I MUST'VE BEEN IMAGINING THINGS.

WELL, MAYBE IT'S JUST ME, BUT SINCE THE FIRE, I'VE HAD A HARD TIME SMELLING ANYTHING BUT SMOKE.

SCRATCH SCRATCH SCRATCH

IT ISN'T JUST YOU.

MAYBE WE SHOULD BOTH BE MORE ALERT, AFTER THE STRANGENESS OUT IN THE FIELD...BUT WE'RE SO TIRED.

THE TIREDNESS GOES AWAY FAST WHEN WE BOTH HEAR SOMETHING.

SKRITCH

RATTLE SKRITCH

WHAT DO YOU THINK IT IS? RACCOON? MAYBE A POSSUM?

NOT SURE.

THE REALIZATION IS SO PAINFUL THAT IT FEELS LIKE MY HEAD'S GOING TO SPLIT IN HALF.

BARLEY WAS RIGHT. FROM THE VERY BEGINNING, HE WAS RIGHT.

AND I'VE BEEN SUCH A FOOL.

SUDDENLY, THOUGHTS OF THE TWOLEG GO RIGHT OUT OF MY HEAD.

ARE YOU IN TROUBLE?

WHAT DO YOU WANT?

WE'RE GOING TO LIVE HERE NOW. YOU'RE NOT WELCOME ANYMORE.

WILLIE PROMISED US A NEW HOME.

HEH. NEVER SHOULD'VE DOUBTED HIM.

AND WE DO **TRY.**

BUT IT HAS BEEN A LONG TIME SINCE EITHER OF US HAS HAD TO FIGHT.

AND THEY OUTNUMBER US TWO TO ONE.

I DON'T KNOW WHERE WE'LL GO OR WHAT WE'LL DO WHEN WE WAKE UP, BUT WITHOUT ANY DESTINATION IN MIND...

...THE HIGHSTONES SEEM AS GOOD A CHOICE AS ANYWHERE ELSE.

WE HEADING UP THERE?

I GUESS.

I DON'T...I...BARLEY, IT'S JUST NOW HITTING ME. I'VE NEVER FIT IN. ANYWHERE.

IS IT ME? IS THERE SOMETHING WRONG WITH ME?

WE'LL FIND ANOTHER FARM. DON'T WORRY.

I TRY. I TRY NOT TO WORRY.

AND I'M ALMOST SUCCESSFUL.

IT TAKES LONGER THAN I THOUGHT IT WOULD TO REACH THE HIGHSTONES. WE'RE ALREADY GETTING TIRED...

...AND THEN THE WEATHER DECIDES NOT TO DO US ANY FAVORS.

ARE WE THERE YET?

ALMOST!

RHOWR. I HAVEN'T BEEN THIS COLD AND WET SINCE...

HUH. I DON'T THINK I'VE EVER BEEN THIS COLD AND WET!

#2: A CLAN IN NEED

THIS WHOLE EXPERIENCE SEEMS LIKE A DREAM TO ME.

GETTING DRIVEN OUT OF THE FARM...COMING HERE TO THE MOONSTONE...SEEING STARCLAN IN A DREAM...

RRAAOWRR!

YOU ALL RIGHT?

JUST...JUST A DREAM.

I DON'T KNOW EVERYTHING ABOUT THAT TIME IN HIS LIFE, BUT I KNOW HIS SISTER ALMOST DIED. SOMETIMES HE RELIVES THAT.

YEAH.

THE SAME ONE? ...ABOUT VIOLET?

WELL, YOU'RE AWAKE NOW...AND WE KNOW VIOLET'S SAFE...AND IT'S TIME TO GO.

THUNDERCLAN'S GOING TO HELP US. STARCLAN TOLD ME SO.

WE CAN FIND ANOTHER HOME, IN ANOTHER BARN, YOU KNOW.

I KNOW WE COULD. IT'S JUST...HOW FAR WILL YOU RUN?

WE WERE CHASED OUT OF OUR HOMES BEFORE-- I LEFT THUNDERCLAN AND YOU FLED FROM BLOODCLAN. WE CAN'T LET IT HAPPEN AGAIN.

THUNDERCLAN WILL HELP US.

FIRESTAR HIMSELF SAID WE SHOULD GO TO HIM IF WE EVER GET IN TROUBLE.

DIDN'T HE?

HRMPH.

LOOK, I KNOW YOU DON'T LIKE BEING AROUND A LOT OF OTHER CATS.

BUT WE'LL GO IN PEACE--AND BE WELCOMED--AND WE WON'T STAY LONG.

FINE, FINE... FINE, WE'LL GO.

AND I WON'T COMPLAIN.

MUCH.

TO GET TO THUNDERCLAN TERRITORY, WE HAVE TO RETRACE OUR STEPS...

...WHICH TAKES US RIGHT PAST THE FARM. OUR RIGHTFUL HOME.

AND THERE THEY ARE: THE ROGUES WHO DROVE US OUT. ACTING AS IF THEY OWN THE PLACE.

IT'S A HARD SIGHT TO TAKE.

WE'LL GET OUR HOME BACK, BARLEY. WE WILL.

YOU'LL SEE.

WE HAVE TO CROSS WINDCLAN TERRITORY, TOO. CROSSING FAMILIAR GROUND LIKE THIS...

...IT TAKES ME BACK TO WHEN I FIRST CAME HERE...AS AN EAGER YOUNG THUNDERCLAN APPRENTICE, ON MY WAY TO HIGHSTONES FOR THE FIRST TIME.

I KNOW WE'RE DOING THE RIGHT THING. I CAN FEEL IT.

SUDDENLY THE SOUND OF MANY RUNNING CATS BREAKS ME OUT OF MY MEMORIES.

WHAT'S THAT?

I DON'T KNOW. BE READY.

WHEN YOU SAID WE WERE GOING TO BE WELCOMED, THIS ISN'T WHAT I HAD IN MIND!

JUST STAY CALM. DON'T MAKE ANY SUDDEN MOVES.

WE'LL BE FINE.

ROGUES! WHAT ARE YOU DOING HERE? DID YOU STEAL OUR KIT?

HUH?

WE DIDN'T STEAL ANYTHING.

HEY! I KNOW YOU. RAVENPAW! RIGHT?

AND IT'S BARLEY, ISN'T IT? WE MET LAST GREENLEAF. I'M MUDCLAW.

THESE CATS ARE NOT OUR ENEMIES. RAVENPAW HERE USED TO BE IN THUNDERCLAN.

HMPH.

SOUNDS LIKE AN ENEMY TO ME.

WHAT'S GOING ON? THERE'S A KIT MISSING?

'FRAID SO. LITTLE DARK GRAY SCRAP NAMED CROWKIT.

CAN'T STAY OUT OF TROUBLE, THAT ONE, AND HE SNEAKED OUT THIS MORNING BEFORE DAWN.

WE'RE ALL A BIT JUMPY AND WORRIED. ROGUES HAVE BEEN CAUSING TROUBLE IN SHADOWCLAN AND THUNDERCLAN TERRITORIES.

EVER SINCE THE BATTLE WITH BLOODCLAN.

WELL, WE'RE ON OUR WAY TO THUNDERCLAN RIGHT NOW, BUT WE'LL DEFINITELY KEEP OUR EYES OPEN FOR YOU.

THANKS!

GOOD-BYE!

THE CLOSER WE GET TO THUNDERCLAN TERRITORY, THE MORE EXCITED I GET. IT'S LIKE A HOMECOMING, SORT OF.

HEY! LET'S GO TO THE CAMP BY WAY OF FOURTREES!

I CAN SHOW YOU WHAT THE GATHERING SPOT IS LIKE WHEN IT'S NOT COVERED UP WITH A BUNCH OF FIGHTING CATS.

UH...YEAH, OKAY.

SEE? ISN'T THIS PLACE GREAT?

I GUESS SO.

AND THERE'S THE GREAT ROCK!

ONCE EVERY FULL MOON, THE CLAN LEADERS STAND UP THERE TO ADDRESS ALL THE CATS.

99

MMM-HMM.

SKRRTCH
SKRRTCH

HEY--
DO YOU HEAR
THAT?

LET ME GUESS.

CROWKIT, RIGHT?

OH--HI!

YOU MIND TELLING
US WHAT IT IS YOU'RE
DOING, EXACTLY?

I WANT TO SEE WHAT
IT'S LIKE TO BE A LEADER!
BUT, UH...

...I CAN'T CLIMB
THE ROCK.

DUSTPELT SOON REALIZES THAT IT DOESN'T MAKE ANY SENSE FOR A SPY TO ASK TO SEE THE CLAN LEADER.

HE AGREES TO TAKE US TO THE CAMP.

ALONG THE WAY WE STOP SO HE CAN DIG UP SOME FRESH-KILL THEY'D BURIED FOR SAFEKEEPING.

THIS IS ALL STARTING TO FEEL SO FAMILIAR! I'VE BURIED PREY BENEATH THAT TREE MYSELF!

AND THE GORSE TUNNEL... THE ENTRANCE TO THE THUNDERCLAN CAMP. SUDDENLY MY HEART SPEEDS UP...!

WHO ARE THEY?

I'VE NEVER SEEN THEM BEFORE!

THAT'S RAVENPAW AND BARLEY. THEY'RE ROGUES, BUT THEY'RE THE BEST KIND OF ROGUES.

THEY HELPED THUNDERCLAN WHEN WE NEEDED IT THE MOST.

WOW...

I RECOGNIZE FIRESTAR'S MATE, SANDSTORM, AT ONCE. BUT THOSE KITS WITH HER...

YOU'VE HAD LITTLE ONES! THEY'RE BEAUTIFUL!

YOU AND FIRESTAR MUST BE SO PROUD!

THAT WE ARE, OLD FRIEND.

RAVENPAW, WELCOME BACK!

LIFE ON THE FARM MUST BE AGREEING WITH YOU.

WELL...

BARLEY, WELCOME TO THUNDERCLAN.

THANK YOU, FIRESTAR.

EVERYTHING SEEMS RIGHT HERE. ESPECIALLY WITH FIRESTAR. THE CATS ALL LOVE HIM.

ARE YOU HUNGRY? THERE'S ENOUGH TO SHARE.

FIRESTAR OBVIOUSLY WANTS TO PUT US AT EASE.

I DECIDE NOT TO BRING UP OUR TROUBLES UNTIL HE'S READY.

I'M GRATEFUL THAT HE DOESN'T WAIT VERY LONG, THOUGH.

WHAT BRINGS YOU TO THUNDERCLAN, RAVENPAW?

I...WELL, YOU SEE, IT'S...

TO MY SURPRISE, THE WORDS WON'T COME. I'VE BEEN AWAY FROM THE CLAN TOO LONG. I'VE FORGOTTEN HOW TO ASK FOR HELP.

I CAN SEE YOU'RE IN TROUBLE. THERE IS NOTHING YOU CAN'T ASK.

THUNDERCLAN REMEMBERS THAT YOU AND BARLEY CAME TO OUR AID TO DEFEAT BLOODCLAN.

WE NEED YOUR HELP, FIRESTAR.

WAS I WRONG TO ASK, FIRESTAR?

NO.

WE'LL DO WHAT WE CAN.

NOW YOU MUST REST IN OUR CAMP.

NEITHER BARLEY NOR I UNDERSTAND WHAT HAPPENED THIS AFTERNOON.

THERE'S SOMETHING WRONG...SOMETHING FIRESTAR ISN'T TELLING US.

I JUST WISH WE KNEW WHAT IT WAS.

GET CINDERPELT!

HURRY!

I WAIT A FEW MINUTES FOR THE PANIC TO DIE DOWN BEFORE I TRY TO FIGURE ANYTHING OUT.

FIRESTAR?

WHAT'S GOING ON? WHAT HAPPENED TO YOUR PATROL?

CATS HAVE BEEN COMING FROM TWOLEGPLACE. LAUNCHING RAIDS ON THUNDERCLAN TERRITORY.

ATTACKING THUNDERCLAN PATROLS AND STEALING PREY.

I HAD HOPED THE TROUBLE WITH TWOLEGPLACE ROGUES WOULD HAVE STOPPED, NOW THAT SCOURGE IS DEAD...

...BUT IT HASN'T. AND THESE RAIDS ARE GETTING MORE FREQUENT.

OUR FIRST PATROL IS THE NEXT MORNING AT DAWN.

TWO STRONG WARRIORS, GRAYSTRIPE AND CLOUDTAIL, ARE READY TO GO AND WAITING FOR US.

OF COURSE, SOME OF US ARE MORE READY TO GO THAN OTHERS. I DON'T THINK BARLEY'S EVER HAD TO WAKE UP THIS EARLY.

COME ON, BARLEY, LET'S GO! THEY'RE WAITING!

JUS' LEMME SLEEP A LITTLE MORE. JUS' A LITTLE SNOOZE.

GET UP!

IT'S A SUCCESSFUL PATROL. WE'VE GOT A DAY'S WORTH OF FRESH-KILL...

...AND WE'RE STARTING TO THINK EVERYTHING'S GOING TO BE QUIET.

WE'RE MISTAKEN ABOUT THAT.

BUT THEN--RIGHT IN THE MIDDLE OF EVERYTHING--

--SOMETHING STRANGE HAPPENS.

BARLEY REACTS AS IF THE CAT WITH THE TORN EAR HADN'T SAID ANYTHING AT ALL...

HEY!

HEY! YOU!

...AND THEN THERE'S NO MORE TIME TO THINK ABOUT IT, AS ANOTHER THUNDERCLAN PATROL ARRIVES.

BACK! BACK NOW!

WE GOT WHAT WE CAME FOR!

WE WATCH THEM GO. THEY'VE STOLEN OR RUINED ALL OF OUR FRESH-KILL.

AND I STILL DON'T KNOW WHAT TO THINK ABOUT THAT CAT WHO SEEMED TO RECOGNIZE BARLEY. DID THEY KNOW EACH OTHER BEFORE?

AND IT TURNS OUT I WASN'T THE ONLY ONE WHO NOTICED, EITHER.

DID YOU KNOW THOSE CATS?

...NO. NO, I DIDN'T.

REALLY? BECAUSE THEY SEEMED TO KNOW YOU.

GRAYSTRIPE DOESN'T GET THE CHANCE TO KEEP ASKING BARLEY QUESTIONS.

MEW!

!

?

BUT I CAN TELL HE'S NOT FINISHED WITH THIS.

"THOSE CATS BACK THERE..."

...YOU KNEW THEM WHEN YOU WERE IN BLOODCLAN, DIDN'T YOU?

THAT PART OF MY LIFE IS OVER.

I DON'T WANT TO TALK ABOUT IT.

THE NEXT DAY COMES, ALONG WITH THE CRYING OF KITS AND THE RUMBLING OF EMPTY BELLIES.

AND BARLEY STILL MIGHT AS WELL BE MADE OF STONE, FOR ALL THE NOISE HE MAKES.

DON'T WORRY, SANDSTORM. WE'RE HEADING OUT NOW. I KNOW WHERE THERE'S SOME GOOD HUNTING.

WE'LL HAVE THOSE KITS FED BEFORE YOU KNOW IT.

GOOD LUCK, YOU TWO!

I KEEP TRYING TO THINK OF THINGS TO SAY TO BARLEY, TO GET HIM TO COME AROUND. BUT THEY ALL SOUND STUPID IN MY HEAD...

...SO I KEEP MY MOUTH SHUT. HOURS PASS...

...AND THEN...

HELP! HELP! I NEED HELP, PLEASE!

RAINPAW! WHAT'S WRONG? WHERE'S YOUR SISTER?

SORRELPAW--IT WAS ROGUES! THEY HURT HER BAD!

PLEASE, FIRESTAR--

--DON'T LET MY SISTER DIE!

WARRIORS! FORM A RESCUE PARTY, NOW!

WE'VE GOT A CLANMATE TO SAVE!

BARLEY... WE SHOULD HELP THEM.

LET'S GO.

MY LITTLE SISTER'S GOING TO BE OKAY, ISN'T SHE?

I HOPE SO, RAINPAW. I HOPE SHE IS.

I TRIED TO PROTECT HER. THEY JUST..., THEY CAME OUT OF NOWHERE...

THEY TRIED TO KILL MY SISTER, TOO.

I'LL... I'LL HELP.

LET'S GO TALK TO FIRESTAR.

THAT NIGHT, FIRESTAR CALLS A COUNCIL OF ALL THE CLAN WARRIORS, AND EVERYONE LISTENS HARD TO WHAT BARLEY HAS TO SAY.

I KNOW HOW DIFFICULT THIS IS FOR HIM. I'M SO PROUD OF HIM FOR DOING IT!

THOSE WERE BLOODCLAN CATS THAT ATTACKED US, BUT IT'S MORE THAN THAT.

THEY WERE SOME OF SCOURGE'S CLOSEST ADVISORS.

BUT I'M PRETTY SURE BARLEY
HATES IT EVEN MORE THAN I DO.

I WANT TO GET CAUGHT UP, VIOLET, I REALLY DO. BUT WE HAVE SOMETHING IMPORTANT WE HAVE TO ASK YOU.

BARLEY FILLS HER IN ON EVERYTHING THAT'S HAPPENED AS QUICKLY AS HE CAN. I HATE TO SEE HER HAPPINESS FADE SO FAST.

I'VE BEEN HEARING RUMORS ABOUT EX-BLOODCLAN CATS GETTING TOGETHER. THEY SAY THEY'RE GETTING ORGANIZED AGAIN.

MY FRIENDS AND I DON'T LEAVE OUR YARDS MUCH, BUT...WORD GETS AROUND. AND--

--SOMETIMES, DOWN THE ALLEYS, I THINK I CAN HEAR FIGHTING.

IT WAS MUCH BETTER AFTER SCOURGE WENT, BUT IT STARTED TO GET BAD AGAIN ABOUT A MOON AGO.

IS THERE ONE CAT IN CHARGE? WHERE DOES HE LIVE?

I DON'T KNOW, BUT I CAN FIND OUT. NO MORE CATS SHOULD SUFFER!

VIOLET IS IMPRESSIVE. SHE'S SO BRAVE, AND POSITIVE!

IT TOOK BARLEY SO LONG TO WORK UP THIS KIND OF COURAGE, BUT SHE'S READY TO GO, ON THE SPOT.

WELL...I GUESS THERE'S NOTHING FOR IT BUT TO DO IT.

COME ON, THIS WAY.

WHERE ARE WE GOING?

TO TALK TO A FRIEND OF MINE.

MITZI?

RRHAOWRR!

VIOLET, YOU ALMOST STARTLED ME TO DEATH!

IT'S NOT POLITE TO SNEAK UP ON A GIRL IN THE MIDDLE OF A GOOD ROLL IN THE GRASS, YOU KNOW!

MITZI, I'D LIKE YOU TO MEET MY BROTHER BARLEY, AND HIS FRIEND RAVENPAW.

WE NEED TO TALK TO YOU ABOUT THE ROGUES AROUND HERE.

IT TURNS OUT MITZI'S HAD MORE TO DO WITH THE ROGUES THAN WE'D KNOWN.

THEY...THEY TOOK MY SON. THOSE MONSTERS FROM BLOODCLAN. THEY JUST TOOK HIM ONE NIGHT, AND I HAVEN'T SEEN HIM SINCE.

I FOLLOWED THEM, FOLLOWED HIS SCENT, BUT I DIDN'T DARE GET CLOSE. THEY'RE RECRUITING A NEW BLOODCLAN NOW, WITH NEW LEADERSHIP.

TAKE US THERE, MITZI. PLEASE.

MAYBE WE CAN FIND YOUR SON.

I-I DON'T KNOW, VIOLET. WHAT CAN YOU THREE DO?

IT WON'T BE JUST US. IF WE CAN FIND OUT WHERE THESE CATS LIVE, THERE ARE MORE WHO WOULD FIGHT THEM, TOO.

A LOT MORE.

WITH MITZI CONVINCED, WE SET OUT... AND THE CLOSER WE GOT TO THIS PLACE, EVEN THOUGH I HADN'T SEEN IT YET, THE TENSER I GOT.

THERE.

FOR S

THAT'S WHERE THEY TOOK HIM.

CATS ON GUARD OUTSIDE...

IT'S HIM. SNIPE.

...IN EXCHANGE FOR YOUR ABSOLUTE LOYALTY.

READY...ON MY SIGNAL...

VIOLET?

WHAT ARE YOU DOING?

HOOT!

JUMPER!

EVERY DROP OF BLOOD IN MY VEINS TURNS TO ICE WHEN THOSE TWO MONSTER CATS TURN AND STARE AT HER.

WHAT IN STARCLAN'S NAME IS SHE DOING?

AND IT'S THAT MOMENT WHEN IT HITS ME, SO HARD MY LEGS FEEL WEAK. THOSE TWO CATS...

...THEY'RE COLORED EXACTLY LIKE BARLEY! THEY'RE BIGGER, TOUGHER-LOOKING, BUT OTHERWISE THEY'RE EXACTLY THE SAME!

WHO'S THERE?

IT'S ME.

VIOLET.

YOUR SISTER.

AND JUST LIKE THAT...

...THE BATTLE'S OVER.

BUT THINGS STILL AREN'T FINISHED.

ALL RIGHT, YOU TWO. VIOLET AND BARLEY.

LET'S SAY YOU'VE GOT OUR ATTENTION NOW. LET'S TALK.

BARLEY...VIOLET. WE HAVE THEM BEATEN. NEITHER OF YOU HAS TO DO ANYTHING.

I THINK WE DO, FIRESTAR. WE HAVE TO TALK TO THEM...

THE SILENCE IN THIS PLACE IS SO SUDDEN, AND SO PROFOUND...

...I THINK I CAN ACTUALLY HEAR THESE ROGUES' ATTITUDES CHANGING.

WAIT! WAIT!

IT'S JUMPER AND HOOT! REMEMBER US?

WE'RE KIN, LIKE YOU SAID! YOU WOULDN'T HURT YOUR OLD LITTERMATES, WOULD YOU?

N-N-NOW HOLD ON.

W-WE CAN MAKE A DEAL!

WHAT DO YOU WANT? NAME IT!

IT'S TOO LATE, JUMPER.

YOU'VE BEEN ATTACKING CLAN CATS AND STEALING FROM THEM. NOW YOU MUST PAY.

NO--NO, YOU'VE GOT IT ALL WRONG!

WE HAVEN'T STOLEN ANY PREY.

BARLEY?

PROTECT US, BROTHER...!

AND WITH THAT, HOOT AND JUMPER WERE GONE.....

A FEW TERRIFIED ROGUES WERE STILL MILLING AROUND BUT THERE WAS ONE IN PARTICULAR WE'D FORGOTTEN ABOUT.

EXCUSE ME.... VI- VIOLET?

WHAT? YOU ROGUES HAVEN'T HAD ENOUGH?

NO! I MEAN...YES. VIOLET, IT'S FRITZ. I USED TO LIVE NEXT DOOR!

YOU'RE MITZI'S SON! ARE YOU OKAY? DID THEY HURT YOU?

THEY BROUGHT ME HERE A MOON AGO AND WOULDN'T LET ME LEAVE! THEY TRIED TO MAKE ME JOIN BLOODCLAN AND TEACH ME TO FIGHT...

BUT I'M NO GOOD AT THAT. I JUST WANT TO GO HOME.

I KNOW THE FEELING...

OH, FRITZ... WE'LL GET YOU HOME. MITZI WILL BE SO HAPPY!

WARRIORS--
WE'RE DONE HERE.

IT'S TIME
TO LEAVE.

WELL...I SUPPOSE IT'S
TIME FOR US TO GO BACK
TO OUR LIVES NOW.

I'M GLAD YOU
HAVE A HOME WHERE YOU
CAN BE SAFE AND HAPPY.

ALL RIGHT...WELL,
I'LL TAKE VIOLET BACK TO
HER PLACE, THEN COME BACK
TO THUNDERCLAN.

OH--I'LL
GO WITH YOU.

NO...NO, THAT'S
NOT NECESSARY.

I'LL TAKE
HER HOME ON MY
OWN.

I CAN ONLY IMAGINE WHAT BARLEY MUST BE THINKING, AND FEELING, RIGHT NOW.

WE CAME HERE TO GET OUR HOME BACK...AND MAYBE, MAYBE...

...HE GOT A PART OF HIS PAST BACK, TOO.

I WANT TO THANK YOU, RAVENPAW. YOU AND BARLEY BOTH.

REALLY, IT WAS... IT WAS NOTHING.

WE BOTH KNOW BETTER THAN THAT. AS SOON AS MY WARRIORS ARE FIT AGAIN, I'LL LEAD A PATROL TO YOUR FARM MYSELF.

WE'LL GET YOU YOUR HOME BACK.

#3: THE HEART OF A WARRIOR

IT'S HARD TO BELIEVE I'M HERE.

BACK IN THE THUNDERCLAN CAMP.

CATS YAWN AND STRETCH ALL AROUND ME AS THEY WAKE UP...

...AND INSTEAD OF DOGS BARKING OR ROOSTERS CROWING, ALL I HEAR IS THE SONG OF BIRDS IN THE FOREST.

MY NAME IS RAVENPAW. MY BEST FRIEND, BARLEY, AND I WERE FORCED OUT OF OUR HOME ON THE FARM BY A GROUP OF ROGUES...

WHAT BROUGHT US HERE WAS PRETTY HORRIBLE...BUT I REALLY DO ENJOY BEING HERE.

...AND WE CAME TO THUNDERCLAN FOR HELP.

I WAS BORN INTO THUNDERCLAN, AFTER ALL.

WATCHING THE HUNTING PATROLS HEADING OUT...

...SEEING THE CLAN CATS TOGETHER, YOUNG AND OLD...

IT'S TAKEN ME LESS TIME THAN I EXPECTED TO GET USED TO ALL THIS AGAIN.

IT'S HARD TO BELIEVE ONLY THREE DAYS HAVE PASSED SINCE BARLEY AND I HELPED THUNDERCLAN DEFEAT SOME OTHER ROGUES...

...A BUNCH OF SCAVENGERS FROM TWOLEGPLACE.

THOSE MANGY CATS WON'T BE AMBUSHING ANY MORE CLAN HUNTING PATROLS NOW.

AND TODAY, FIRESTAR'S MAKING GOOD ON HIS PROMISE.

HE'S GOING TO HELP BARLEY AND ME RECLAIM OUR FARM.

TODAY, BARLEY AND I ARE GOING HOME!

WE OWE HIM SO MUCH FOR AGREEING TO HELP US TAKE BACK THE FARM.

THERE'S FIRESTAR NOW.

READY?

YES!

IT'S TIME!

HRRRRK...DO WE HAVE TO LEAVE SO EARLY?

RAVENPAW. BARLEY. THUNDERCLAN WILL MISS YOU BOTH.

ARE YOU SURE YOU CAN'T WAIT A LITTLE LONGER? THERE ARE MANY CATS THAT WOULD WISH TO SAY FAREWELL.

I'D PREFER TO GO QUIETLY, IF WE COULD. NOT HAVE ANY BIG FUSS.

I'M NOT ONE FOR BIG FAREWELLS.

THAT MIGHT BE BEST, YES.

AS YOU WISH, THEN.

LET'S GO TAKE BACK YOUR HOME.

SANDSTORM'S WARNING COMES TOO LATE. SQUIRRELKIT'S RUCKUS WAKES EVERYONE UP.

THEY COME TO SEE WHAT SQUIRRELKIT'S MAKING ALL THE NOISE ABOUT...

...AND HERE WE ARE. RIGHT OUT IN THE OPEN. OBVIOUSLY ABOUT TO LEAVE.

BARLEY'S HANDLING ALL THE ATTENTION A LITTLE BETTER THAN I THOUGHT HE WOULD, ACTUALLY.

ALL RIGHT, EVERYONE. LET US THROUGH.

IT'S TIME TO GO.

THUNDERCLAN'S GOOD-BYES AND THANK-YOUS RING IN MY EARS AS WE TRAVEL.

PART OF ME WANTS TO STAY... BUT ONLY A SMALL PART.

FORMER THUNDERCLAN CAT OR NOT, I BELONG ON THE FARM.

RUNNING THROUGH THE FOREST, THOUGH, AS PART OF A WARRIOR PATROL...THAT'S HARD TO BEAT.

WARRIORS--HOLD UP. BE READY.

NO, GRAYSTRIPE... THERE'S NO NEED.

OUR FRIENDS FROM WINDCLAN ARE EXPECTING US.

DEADFOOT. GOOD TO SEE YOU.

AND YOU, FIRESTAR.

RAVENPAW...BARLEY. WE'VE HEARD ABOUT WHAT HAPPENED AT THE FARM.

GOOD LUCK TO YOU BOTH. YOU DESERVE TO GET YOUR HOME BACK.

THANK YOU...THAT MEANS A LOT!

LOOKS LIKE WE HAVE FRIENDS IN MORE THAN ONE CLAN NOW...!

WE DON'T GET ANY MORE SURPRISES ON THE TRIP, GOOD OR BAD.

JUST LOTS OF RUNNING. LOTS OF TIME TO THINK...AND THE MORE I THINK, THE MORE NERVOUS I GET.

BY THE TIME WE REACH THE FARM, I THINK I'M ABOUT AS NERVOUS AS I COULD POSSIBLY BE.

LOOK AT THAT. THEY FIXED THE BARN AFTER THE FIRE...

THAT HALF-RUINED BUILDING ON THE EDGE OF THE FAR FIELD. WHAT IS THAT?

USED TO BE A COWSHED. NOW IT'S ABANDONED.

GOOD. WE'LL SET UP CAMP THERE.

CLOUDTAIL--TAKE A HUNTING PATROL OUT, BUT KEEP YOUR DISTANCE FROM THE FARM.

SURE THING.

THE REST OF YOU, STICK WITH RAVENPAW AND ME.

RAVENPAW, I'D LIKE TO SCOUT THE FARMYARD. WOULD YOU SHOW US THE WAY?

OF COURSE.

WE KEEP OUR NOSES TO THE WIND, ALERT FOR THE ROGUES' SCENT.

WE CAN'T LET THEM KNOW WE'RE HERE.

NOT YET.

"THESE ROGUES ARE RUTHLESS. THEY FORCED US OUT OF HERE WITH A MIX OF SAVAGERY AND DIRTY TRICKS."

"PLUS, WELL...THEY OUTNUMBERED US PRETTY BADLY, TOO."

YOU WERE RIGHT TO ASK US FOR HELP. EVEN IF YOU HADN'T BEEN OUTNUMBERED, FROM THE LOOKS OF THEM...

...THERE'S NO WAY THAT WOULD HAVE BEEN A CLEAN, FAIR FIGHT.

OKAY. NOW THAT THOSE TWO ARE OUT OF THE WAY I WANT A LOOK INSIDE THAT BARN.

QUICKLY NOW. GO.

IT BREAKS MY HEART, WHAT GREETS US INSIDE THE BARN. THIS PLACE USED TO BE OUR HOME.

NOW IT'S A WRECK...AND IT STINKS OF STALE BEDDING AND CAT DIRT.

WE HEAR SOMEONE SNORING. SLEEPING, INSTEAD OF TAKING CARE OF WHERE THEY LIVE.

NOT ONLY THAT...BUT THOSE KITS ARE PLAYING WITH THEIR PREY. I DON'T THINK THEY'RE EVEN GOING TO EAT IT.

HOW WASTEFUL. HOW WRONG.

THE WARRIOR CODE FORBIDS WASTING FOOD LIKE THIS. I'M NO WARRIOR-- I DON'T HAVE TO LIVE BY THE CODE...

...BUT THIS MAKES ME SO ANGRY, I BARELY HEAR FIRESTAR CALLING FOR US TO LEAVE, THE BLOOD'S RUSHING SO LOUD IN MY EARS.

THE CHICKENS DON'T LIKE THE ROGUES...WILLIE AND HIS CREW KILLED SOME OF THEIR CHICKS RIGHT BEFORE WE LEFT.

BUT THEY ALWAYS LIKED RAVENPAW AND ME. THEY SHOULDN'T BE ANY TROUBLE.

ALL RIGHT. WE'LL WAIT FOR THE ROGUES TO SETTLE DOWN FOR THE NIGHT.

THEN WE'LL GO UNDER THE DOOR AGAIN AND AMBUSH THEM AS THEY SLEEP.

UNTIL THEN WE MUST STAY HIDDEN.

DO NOT LEAVE THIS SHED.

THAT'S NO TROUBLE. OUR PATROL BROUGHT BACK PLENTY OF FRESH-KILL. WE CAN STAY HERE JUST FINE.

IT'S TENSE, ALL THE WAITING.

SEVERAL OF THE OTHER CATS GET SOME SLEEP, BUT I CAN'T.

POOR BARLEY. HE'S LOOKING... OLDER. THIS WAS HIS HOME BEFORE IT WAS MINE.

THIS MUST BE SO HARD ON HIM.

VIOLET...

RAVENPAW. YOU OKAY?

YEAH, I'M FINE. JUST A LITTLE NERVOUS.

I OWE THIS TO BARLEY. I NEED TO MAKE HIS HOME SAFE AGAIN. HE WAS SO GENEROUS TO ME WHEN I NEEDED HELP.

DON'T WORRY, OLD FRIEND. WE'LL MAKE THIS RIGHT.

WE CAN HEAR THE TWOLEGS START TO FEED THE COWS AND THE CHICKENS.

THESE ARE THE LAST THINGS THEY DO BEFORE SUNDOWN.

IT'S ALMOST TIME.

EXCEPT FOR THE DISTANT HOOT OF AN OWL, THE FARM IS SILENT AND STILL.

SO FAR, SO GOOD.

I WONDER IF THE DOGS REMEMBER HOW BARLEY AND I SAVED THEIR LIVES DURING THE FIRE HERE.

RRRRHH?

ZZZZZ...

PROBABLY NOT.

IT SEEMS LIKE THE PLAN'S GOING TO GO OFF WITHOUT A HITCH...

BUK KWAAWK!

...UNTIL THE CHICKENS GIVE US A NASTY SURPRISE.

BUK KWAAWK!

BUK KWAAWK

WHAT'S GOING ON?

I DON'T KNOW! THEY NEVER USED TO BE THIS NERVOUS!

IT'S SNAPPER! HE MUST TAUNT THEM ALL THE TIME!

NOW THEY'RE SCARED OF ALL CATS!

THIS IS NO GOOD! THEY'RE TOO LOUD! EVERYONE, GO BACK!

RRH?

INTRUDERS!

NO POINT IN RETREATING NOW.

ATTACK!

WARRIORS OF THUNDERCLAN...

AND JUST LIKE THAT, NOT ONLY IS OUR CAREFUL PLAN GONE, BUT I'M FIGHTING, AND I CAN'T EVEN TELL WHO'S WHO!

RAAOWR!

I JUST HOPE WHOEVER I'M SLASHING IS AN ENEMY, AND NOT A FRIEND.

FINALLY...

...MY EYES ADJUST ENOUGH TO SEE...

...AND I ALMOST WISH THEY HADN'T.

THERE ARE CATS HERE THAT I'VE NEVER SEEN BEFORE!

AND THEN...

THIS WAY, JUMPER!

GET HIM, HOOT!

THERE ARE TOO MANY OF THEM!

THUNDERCLAN-- SCATTER! YOU KNOW WHERE TO MEET UP!

I CAN'T BELIEVE IT. IT'S LIKE A NIGHTMARE.

...I KNOW IT'S A LOT WORSE FOR BARLEY.

MY BROTHERS ARE HERE! I CAN'T GET AWAY FROM THEM... NO MATTER WHERE I GO, THEY WON'T LEAVE ME ALONE!

AND THEY'VE BROUGHT BLOODCLAN CATS TO OUR FARM!

BUT AS BAD AS IT IS FOR ME...

I'VE GOT TO DO SOMETHING.

NOW...LISTEN...THIS IS TERRIBLE, I'M NOT SAYING IT'S NOT. BUT IT MIGHT NOT BE AS BAD AS WE THINK.

THEY MIGHT NOT THINK OF THEMSELVES AS BLOODCLAN ANYMORE...AND IF SO, THAT MEANS THEY'RE VULNERABLE.

THOSE CATS WERE CALLING YOUR BROTHERS "JUMPER" AND "HOOT," NOT THEIR BLOODCLAN NAMES.

ONCE A CAT FEARS HIS OWN WEAKNESS, HE'S LOST THE BATTLE BEFORE IT EVEN BEGINS.

I KNOW THIS IS TRUE.

I WAS TERRIFIED OF TIGERCLAW... AND I LET HIM BULLY ME AND THREATEN ME BECAUSE OF IT.

BARLEY AND I BELONG HERE.

THOSE ROGUES ARE WRONG. DEAD WRONG. AND THEY DESERVE TO BE DRIVEN OUT.

THIS IS OUR HOME, AND WE HAVE JUST AS MUCH A RIGHT TO IT AS THE CLANS HAVE A RIGHT TO LIVE IN THE FOREST.

AND BLOODCLAN CATS OR NOT, WE HAVE TO TAKE THIS PLACE BACK.

I SEE FIRESTAR WATCHING ME, AND I REALIZE THAT, IN A LOT OF WAYS, I AM STILL A CLAN CAT.

I DEFINITELY HAVE A SENSE OF HONOR, AND DUTY AND JUSTICE.

BUT I'M TALKING MAINLY FOR BARLEY'S BENEFIT HERE. I NEED HIM TO FEEL THE SAME WAY.

AND TO HAVE THE COURAGE TO FIGHT HIS OWN KIN.

THE CLOUDS HANG LOW AND HEAVY THE NEXT DAY. I KEEP WAITING FOR IT TO RAIN, BUT IT NEVER DOES.

NO ONE'S LEFT THE BARN SINCE SUNUP.

WE USE THE TIME TO COME UP WITH A NEW PLAN OF ATTACK...

...AND I TRY NOT TO LET MY NERVES GET THE BEST OF ME.

FROM HERE THE PLACE LOOKS DESERTED.

THE BLOODCLAN CATS CHANGE EVERYTHING.

IS THERE ANY OTHER WAY INTO THE BARN BESIDES UNDER THE DOOR?

WELL...YES. YES, THERE IS!

THERE ARE HOLES IN THE ROOF, LEADING ONTO THE RAFTERS!

JUST THEN WE ALL NOTICE SOMETHING INTERESTING:

SNAPPER AND POUNCE TAKE OFF AS IF THEY ARE BEING CHASED BY FOXES.

COME ON! LET'S GET 'EM!

NO. STAY.

THEY KNOW THE TERRAIN. WITH THAT BIG OF A HEAD START, WE'D NEVER CATCH THEM.

WELL...GOOD RIDDANCE, I SAY.

THIS JUST SHOWS HOW SCARED THEY ARE--THEY CAN'T EVEN KEEP THEIR OWN FROM DESERTING.

...WE'LL SEE.

FINALLY WE COME UP WITH A PLAN. I THINK IT'S A GOOD ONE... IF NOTHING MESSES IT UP.

EVERYONE, LISTEN TO ME.

IT'S GOING TO HAPPEN LIKE THIS...

FIRESTAR EXPLAINS HIS PLAN QUICKLY AND CLEARLY. WE'LL BE ATTACKING ON TWO FRONTS.

SINCE THE DOOR WILL BE GUARDED, WE'LL SEND TWO CATS TO THE FRONT DOOR...

...THEN WE'LL SLIP DOWN THROUGH THE ROOF AND CATCH THEM BY SURPRISE.

THIS WILL WORK.

WE *WILL* DRIVE THEM OUT THIS TIME.

"IT'S CLEAR."

LET'S GO.

NONE OF US MAKES A SOUND...

...AND THERE'S BRACKENFUR AND BRAMBLEPAW. BUT-!

THEY'RE TOO CLOSE TO THE CHICKENS! THEY'LL SET THEM TO SQUAWKING AGAIN!

DON'T WORRY. THEY KNOW WHAT THEY'RE DOING.

NOW--SHOW US A WAY IN!

THE CHICKENS ARE A PERFECT DISTRACTION! I SHOULD'VE KNOWN BETTER THAN TO QUESTION FIRESTAR.

RIGHT! THERE ARE GAPS IN THE ROOF, RIGHT OVER...

OH NO...

IT'S A HORRIBLE FEELING, THOUGH, WHEN I REALIZE I'M MESSING UP THE PLAN MYSELF.

THE ROOF'S BEEN MENDED SINCE THE FIRE!

THE HOLE WE USED TO CLIMB THROUGH--IT'S NOT HERE ANYMORE!

WHAT DO WE DO?

EVERYONE'S COUNTING ON US!

WE MAKE A HOLE.

TEAR

CRACK

POP

214

THE ROGUES MAY OUTNUMBER US. BUT THEY CAN'T OUTFIGHT US.

REEEOOOWRRRR!

SO MANY OF THE ROGUES HAVE ALREADY RUN AWAY...

WE'RE LEFT WITH ONLY A FEW OF THEM.

BUT THERE'S ONE THAT I'M GLAD TO SEE. ONE I HAVE PERSONAL BUSINESS WITH.

GO, WILLIE. GET OUT OF HERE.

THIS IS NOT YOUR HOME.

WARRIORS!

RETREAT AND REGROUP!

I STILL HAVE FAITH IN FIRESTAR. I KNOW IF HE CAN GET US TO SAFETY, WE CAN FIGURE OUT A WAY TO DEAL WITH THIS.

BUT GETTING US TO SAFETY...

...ALL OF A SUDDEN...

...ISN'T LOOKING TOO LIKELY.

222

I DON'T EVEN HAVE THE WORDS TO DESCRIBE THE FURY THE DOGS UNLEASH ON THE ROGUES.

AS FIERCE AND VICIOUS AS THE ROGUES ARE, THE DOGS ARE SO MUCH MORE TERRIBLE...

...IT'S LIKE WATCHING A FOREST FIRE.

RUN! WE'VE GOT TO RUN!

WHAT?

NO--NO, WAIT!

FIND YOUR MOTHER AND GET LOST! THIS IS NO FIGHT FOR KITS!

ALMOST BEFORE I KNOW IT...

...I'VE GOT WILLIE PINNED.

BUT I DON'T GET THE CHANCE TO ENJOY IT.

RRHAOWR! HELP US!

I CAN SEE THE CONFLICT IN BARLEY AS CLEARLY AS I CAN SEE THE STARS IN THE SKY.

HE CAN'T JUST SEND THESE ROGUES TO THEIR DEATHS.

LIKE IT OR NOT, THEY ARE FAMILY.

IT'S ALL RIGHT, FIRESTAR. IF BARLEY WANTS THEM TO STAY...

...I'LL MAKE SURE THERE AREN'T ANY PROBLEMS.

WELL...IF YOU'RE BOTH SURE...

I CAN ONLY IMAGINE WHAT THIS MUST BE LIKE FOR BARLEY.

LOSING HIS HOME...

DEALING WITH HIS BROTHERS...

HE LOOKS FRAILER THAN EVER.

IS THIS EVEN THE SAME PLACE, RAVENPAW?

I...I BARELY RECOGNIZE IT.

DON'T WORRY, BARLEY. WE'LL MAKE IT RIGHT AGAIN.

JUST LIKE OLD TIMES.

THANKS.

I GUESS THEY'RE READY TO GO BACK TO THEIR CAMP.

YEAH. WE'D BETTER SAY GOOD-BYE.

THANK YOU, FIRESTAR.

EVERYONE, THANK YOU. YOU RISKED YOUR LIVES FOR US.

AS I WAKE UP, THE SOUNDS COME BACK TO ME.

THE COWS AND CHICKENS... THE TWOLEGS...THE CREAK OF THE BARN'S WOODEN WALLS...

WELL, ALMOST EVERYTHING. HOOT AND JUMPER ARE HERE NOW. WE'RE BACK...

I'M HOME AGAIN! I'M HOME, AND BARLEY IS HERE WITH ME, AND EVERYTHING IS RIGHT IN THE WORLD.

...BUT I WONDER...CAN THINGS EVER BE THE SAME AGAIN?

AS SOON AS I'M OUT OF SIGHT-- JUST GOING TO CATCH A MOUSE FOR BREAKFAST--I HEAR THEM TALKING TO BARLEY.

REMEMBER, BARLEY? REMEMBER ALL THE FUN WE USED TO HAVE PLAYING WHEN WE WERE ALL KITS?

YEAH, REMEMBER HOW WE USED TO HIDE FROM EACH OTHER? THOSE WERE THE GREATEST TIMES!

BARLEY DOESN'T EVEN RESPOND. HE LOOKS SO OLD, AND WEAK. ...MAYBE HE JUST NEEDS SOME TIME TO RECOVER FROM ALL THIS.

GOOD MORNING, EVERYONE.

HEY, BARLEY, LISTEN. IT'S A BEAUTIFUL DAY OUTSIDE. WHY DON'T YOU GO FOR A NICE RELAXING WALK?

I CAN STAY AND START SHOWING YOUR BROTHERS AROUND THE FARM.

YOU KNOW--ALL OUR BEST HUNTING AND SNOOZING SPOTS.

AS I WATCH HIM GO, I CAN'T HELP WONDERING EXACTLY WHAT I'VE GOTTEN MYSELF INTO WITH THESE TWO.

THANKS, RAVENPAW. THAT SOUNDS GREAT.

I WON'T BE GONE TOO LONG.

AS IT TURNS OUT, I CAN BEST DESCRIBE BARLEY'S BROTHERS IN ONE WORD: LAZY.

I SHOW THEM THE BEST SPOTS TO HUNT...

I SHOW THEM WHERE TO TAKE THEIR DIRTY STRAW...

I SHOW THEM HOW TO PUT TOGETHER THE MOST COMFORTABLE NEST....

I EVEN SHOW THEM WHERE TO COLLECT MEDICINAL HERBS, LIKE TANSY AND POPPY SEED AND MINT.

BUT THEY DON'T SEEM TO WANT TO DO ANYTHING. THEY JUST WANT EVERYTHING HANDED TO THEM.

I TRY TO SEE THE GOOD IN THEM, FOR BARLEY'S SAKE, BUT THEY'VE GOT A LONG WAY TO GO.

THE LAST THING I SHOW THEM IS UNDERNEATH THE CHICKEN COOP...

...WHERE WE CAN GATHER UP SOME OF THE TASTY GRAIN THAT FALLS THROUGH.

AFTER THAT, I'M DONE. IT'S BEEN A LONG, HARD DAY, AFTER A WHOLE LOT OF LONG, HARD DAYS, AND I AM EXHAUSTED.

I'M BEAT. I'M GOING TO TAKE A NAP.

IF BARLEY COMES BACK BEFORE I WAKE UP, JUST TELL HIM WHERE I AM, OKAY?

I CAN...BARELY KEEP MY EYES OPEN...

I HAVE NO IDEA HOW LONG I'VE BEEN ASLEEP.

BUT I CAN TELL IMMEDIATELY THAT IT'S BARLEY SHAKING ME AWAKE.

WHAT? WHAT? WHAT'S WRONG?

TAKE A LOOK AROUND! YOU TELL ME WHAT'S WRONG!

WH...WHAT?

HOOT! JUMPER!

243

WHAT DID YOU DO? WHY HAVE YOU WRECKED THE PLACE LIKE THIS?

WE WERE ONLY TRYING TO CATCH MICE, RAVENPAW. IT'S DIFFICULT!

YEAH!

WE REALLY NEED SOMEONE TO SHOW US HOW, YOU KNOW.

WHAT'RE YOU TALKING AB--

BARLEY, I DID SHOW THEM! I SPENT ALL DAY SHOWING THEM!

I CAN'T HEAR WHAT HOOT WHISPERS IN BARLEY'S EAR.

BUT I DON'T HAVE TO KNOW THE WORDS TO GET THE GIST OF IT.

BARLEY?

BARLEY. WHAT'S GOING ON?

HOOT SAYS YOU GOT HIM AND JUMPER TO COLLECT ALL THE HERBS AND SUPPLIES WHILE YOU TOOK A NAP.

TH-THAT'S NOT TRUE!

THEY'RE LYING!

LOOK, I CAN TELL YOU'RE EXHAUSTED. I'M SURE YOU DON'T WANT ANY TROUBLE. I KNOW I DON'T.

YOU JUST WANT TO REST, RIGHT?

I CAN'T BELIEVE BARLEY WOULD BELIEVE THEM OVER ME, EVEN FOR A HEARTBEAT!

IT FLUSTERS ME SO BADLY, I CAN'T EVEN SAY ANYTHING. BUT I DO KNOW THIS:

I AM *SICK* OF THOSE TWO.

YOU KNOW, BARLEY...

THIS PLACE IS MUCH NICER, NOW THAT WE'RE HERE WITH FAMILY.

YEAH! LIVING HERE WITH YOU IS GREAT.

A LOT BETTER THAN SHARING THIS SPACE WITH OTHER CATS.

I'VE GOT A GREAT IDEA, BARLEY. COME AND GO FOR A WALK WITH US--

--JUST THE THREE OF US. THREE BROTHERS.

YEAH, GOOD IDEA, HOOT--LET'S GET CAUGHT UP.

FIND OUT WHAT'S BEEN GOING ON IN OUR BROTHER'S LIFE.

...ALL RIGHT. IT'S A NICE NIGHT FOR IT.

WE'LL, UH... WE'LL BE BACK LATER, RAVENPAW.

NO NEED TO STAY UP WAITING.

HOW CAN THIS BE HAPPENING?

HOOT AND JUMPER WERE IN BLOODCLAN! THEY TRIED TO KILL THEIR OWN SISTER!

CAN BLOOD RELATIONS REALLY BE THAT IMPORTANT?

DON'T WAIT UP, HE SAYS.

HRMPH.

WHEN THEY COME BACK, THEY'RE LAUGHING AND JOKING WITH ONE ANOTHER...JUST LIKE FAMILY. JUST LIKE BROTHERS.

MAYBE BLOOD IS THAT IMPORTANT. MAYBE IT CAN OVERCOME ANYTHING. BUT IF BARLEY IS CHOOSING THEM...

...WHERE DOES THAT LEAVE ME? ...WHAT PLACE DO I HAVE HERE?

HEY, RAVENPAW, CATCH US SOME DINNER, WOULD YOU?

I CAN'T COMPETE WITH THEM. THAT MUCH IS BECOMING OBVIOUS.

EASIER TO JUST...DO AS THEY ASK, I GUESS.

WE'RE STILL GETTING CAUGHT UP WITH BARLEY.

YEAH--IT'S NO PROBLEM.

I'LL GET A MOUSE.

NATURALLY IT DOESN'T TAKE MUCH EFFORT TO CATCH A MEAL. BUT I'M NOT PREPARED FOR WHAT HAPPENS NEXT.

THERE HE IS.

ABOUT TIME.

SO, HEY, WE CAN SLEEP IN YOUR NEST TONIGHT, RIGHT? YOU DON'T MIND, DO YOU?

YEAH--WE'D MAKE OUR OWN, BUT THAT WHOLE CARRYING MOSS UNDER OUR CHINS THING...

WE DON'T HAVE THE HANG OF THAT YET.

PART OF ME WANTS TO CALL THEM LAZY AND WORTHLESS, AND DEMAND THAT THEY GET OUT OF MY NEST.

BUT I DON'T WANT TO CAUSE MORE TROUBLE FOR BARLEY.

SURE... ALL RIGHT.

I CAN ALWAYS MAKE ANOTHER.

I HAVE SORT OF A FAINT HOPE THAT THINGS WILL BE BETTER IN THE MORNING.

GUESS I SHOULD'VE KNOWN BETTER.

HEY, RAVENPAW!

IT'S ALL I CAN DO NOT TO RUSH OVER THERE. STAND BY BARLEY'S SIDE.

BUT THIS IS HIS FIGHT, NOT MINE.

BARLEY NEEDS TO SETTLE THIS ON HIS OWN.

RID HIMSELF OF HIS BROTHERS ONCE AND FOR ALL.

HMPH. WE WERE NEVER GOING TO STAY HERE ANYWAY.

IT'S FILTHY, AND WHO WANTS TO EAT DUSTY MICE? WE CAN FIND BETTER FOOD SOMEPLACE ELSE.

WE'RE NOT SCARED OF YOU, BARLEY. IN FACT, WE THINK YOU'RE PATHETIC.

HOOT...JUMPER.

I PITY YOU.

WHAT?

YOU'VE ONLY GOT EACH OTHER NOW. NO OTHER FRIENDS. NO OTHER FAMILY. AND YOU HAVE NO IDEA WHAT LOYALTY MEANS.

HOW LONG WILL YOU LAST OUT THERE? HOW LONG BEFORE YOU TURN ON EACH OTHER?

BARLEY...

I'M SO HAPPY... SO RELIEVED... TO SEE THEM GO.

I'M SO SORRY, RAVENPAW.

I REALLY WANTED TO BELIEVE THEY'D CHANGED.

DON'T APOLOGIZE. I'M VERY PROUD OF WHAT YOU JUST DID.

...I KNOW IT MUST HAVE BEEN HARD.

YOU...YOU DIDN'T HAVE TO SEND THEM AWAY JUST BECAUSE OF ME.

ERIN
HUNTER

is inspired by a love of cats and a fascination with the ferocity of the natural world. As well as having great respect for nature in all its forms, Erin enjoys creating rich mythical explanations for animal behavior. She is also the author of the Seekers, Survivors, and Bravelands series.